Viv the Vet
and
Top Dog

Maverick
Early Readers

'Viv the Vet' and 'Top Dog'
An original concept by Katie Dale
© Katie Dale

Illustrated by Giusi Capizzi

Published by MAVERICK ARTS PUBLISHING LTD

Studio 3A, City Business Centre, 6 Brighton Road,

Horsham, West Sussex, RH13 5BB

© Maverick Arts Publishing Limited May 2018

+44 (0)1403 256941

A CIP catalogue record for this book is available at the British Library.

ISBN 978-1-84886-347-7

Maverick

www.maverickbooks.co.uk

This book is rated as: Red Band (Guided Reading)
This story is decodable at Letters and Sounds Phase 2.

Viv the Vet
and
Top Dog

By **Katie Dale**

Illustrated by **Giusi Capizzi**

The Letter V

Trace the lower and upper case letter with a finger. Sound out the letter.

Down,
up

Down,
up

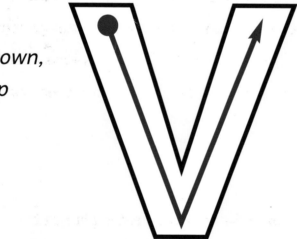

Some words to familiarise:

parrot   vet   rabbit

High-frequency words:

is   go   the   to   I   you

Tips for Reading 'Viv the Vet'

- Practise the words listed above before reading the story.

- If the reader struggles with any of the other words, ask them to look for sounds they know in the word. Encourage them to sound out the words and help them read the words if necessary.

- After reading the story, ask the reader who needed help at the end of the story.

Fun Activity

Can you think of any other animals a vet might help?

Viv the Vet

Pip's parrot is sick.

Quick, go to Viv the vet!

7

Kim's kitten is stuck.

Quick, go to Viv the vet!

Help!

Ron's rabbit is ill.

Quick, go to Viv the vet!

Dan's dog is hurt.

Quick, go to Viv the vet!

Viv's van is stuck!

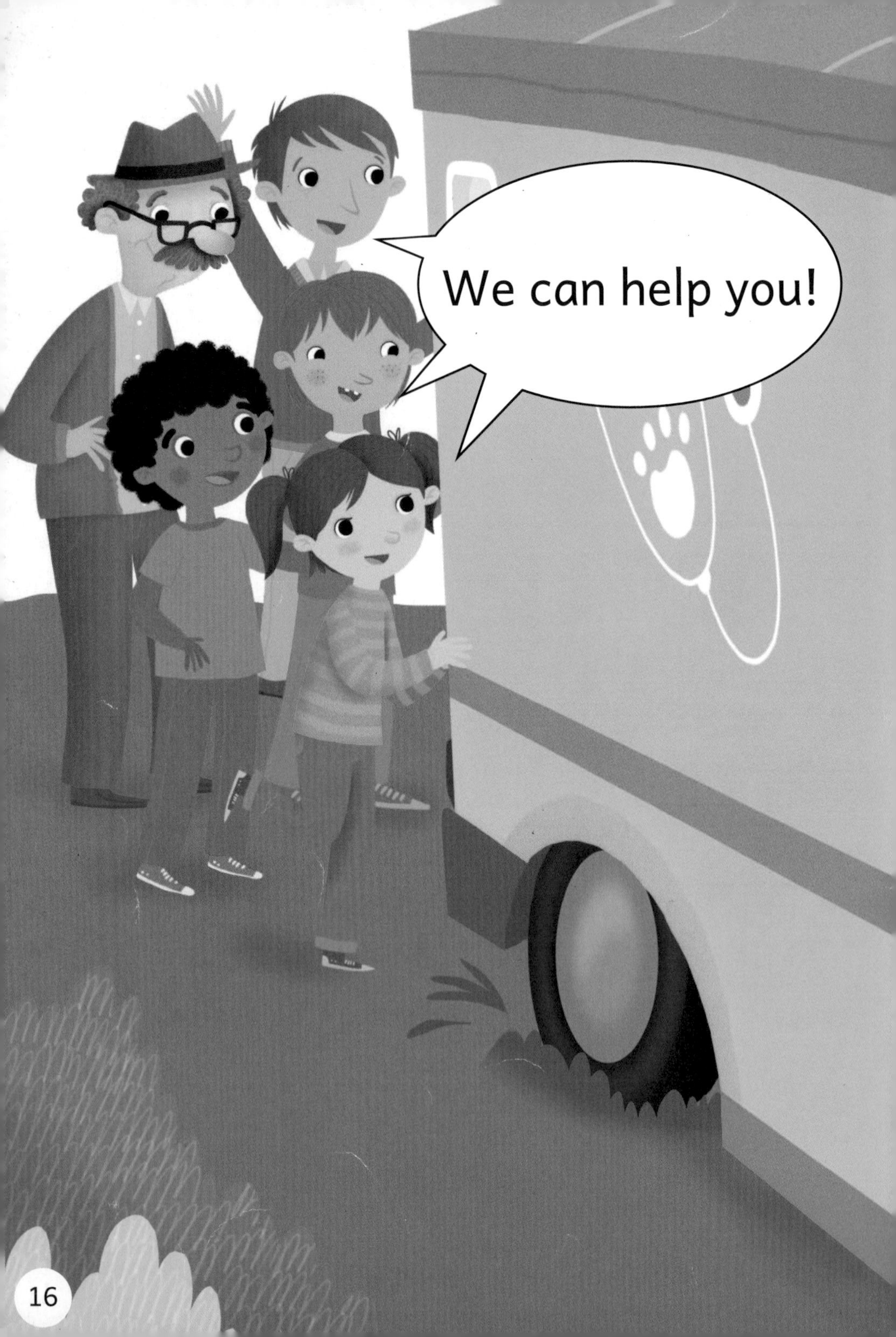
We can help you!

The Letter O

Trace the lower and upper case letter with a finger. Sound out the letter.

Around

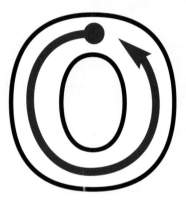

Around

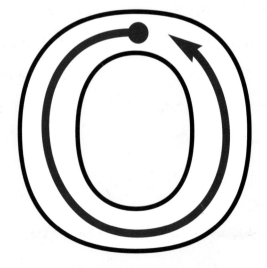

Some words to familiarise:

fluffy strong quick

High-frequency words:

I the are you my

Tips for Reading 'Top Dog'

- Practise the words listed above before reading the story.

- If the reader struggles with any of the other words, ask them to look for sounds they know in the word. Encourage them to sound out the words and help them read the words if necessary.

- After reading the story, ask the reader if they remember why each dog was a top dog.

Fun Activity

Ask the reader which is their favourite dog.

Top Dog

"I am the top dog!" said Lilly.

"I am fluffy."

"I am the top dog!" said Biff.

"I am strong!"

"I am the top dog!" said Dash.

"I am quick!"

"I am not the top dog," said Scruff.

"I am not fluffy."

"I am not strong. I am not quick."

"You are the top dog, Scruff,"
said Viv."You are my dog."

"Woof!" said Scruff.

Book Bands for Guided Reading

Pink   Red   Yellow   Blue   Green   Orange   Turquoise   Purple

Red

Dog in a Dress and Run, Tom, Run!	Buzz and Jump! Jump!	Bam-Boo and I Wish	Sam the Star and Clown Fun!	Seeds and Stuck in the Tree
978-1-84886-290-6	978-1-84886-250-0	978-1-84886-251-7	978-1-84886-288-3	978-1-84886-289-0
Viv the Vet and Top Dog	Go Away! and Let's Make A Rocket	Catch It, Jess! and Cat Nap	Grandad's Cake and Grandad's Pot	Zoom! and Come Back, Mack!
978-1-84886-347-7	978-1-84886-350-7	978-1-84886-348-4	978-1-84886-351-4	978-1-84886-349-1

Plus many more titles in the scheme!

To view the whole Maverick Readers scheme, please visit:

www.maverickbooks.co.uk/early-readers

The Institute of Education book banding system is a scale of colours that reflects the various levels of reading difficulty. The bands are assigned by taking into account the content, the language style, the layout and phonics.

Maverick Early Readers are a bright, attractive range of books covering the pink to purple bands. All of these books have been book banded for guided reading to the industry standard and edited by a leading educational consultant.